BASIC RULES OF GRAMMAR

BOOK 2

Folens Publishers

	Beginning	Book 1	Book 2	Book 3	Book 4
Adjectives and descriptions	35, 36, 40	29, 30, 31, 34, 41, 48	29, 30, 31, 34	11, 12, 13, 14, 15, 18	11, 13, 18
Adverbs			41, 48	22, 23, 26	15, 16, 18
Alphabet	44, 45	44, 45, 46, 48	27, 28, 34	38, 40	17, 18
Antonyms (opposites)	37		35, 36, 40, 48	16, 18	
Apostrophes				24, 25, 26, 46, 48	22, 26, 46
Capital letters		6, 7, 8, 10	6, 10	27, 34, 46, 48	7, 46, 48
Classification/Sorting	33, 34		37, 40		23, 26
Colloquialisms					29, 34
Commas		35, 40	39	45, 48	20, 21, 26
Conjunctions		14, 18	42, 48	37, 40	25, 26
Exclamation marks				31, 34	32
Full stops		6, 7	5, 6, 10	46, 48	19, 46
Homonyms/Homophones/ Commonly confused words		42, 48	38, 40	35, 36, 40	24, 41, 48
Instructions/Information				44	37, 39, 40
Nouns		13, 15			
common	4, 5, 8, 9, 10	16, 17, 18, 19, 20, 21, 25, 26, 37, 40	11, 12, 18	4, 6, 10	4, 10, 42
proper		23, 24, 25, 26	13, 14, 18	4, 10, 27	4, 10
collective					5, 6, 10
Paragraphs					38
Prefixes/Suffixes			46	41, 42, 48	43, 44, 45, 46, 48
Prepositions	14, 15, 16, 17, 18	36, 40	43	39, 40	
Pronouns			16, 18	7, 10	9, 10
Questions/Answers	19, 20, 21, 22, 23, 26	32, 33, 34	24, 25, 26	28, 31, 32, 34	31, 33
Rhyme	46, 48	43, 48		33, 34	
Sentences/Sequencing	6, 7, 10, 11, 12, 13, 18, 24, 25, 27, 28, 30, 31, 32, 34	4, 5, 6, 7, 9, 10, 11	4, 7, 8, 9, 10	17, 44, 47	12, 35, 36, 37, 39, 40
Similes				9, 10	23, 28, 34
Singular/Plural	29, 34	22, 26	15, 18	5	8, 10
Speech/Dialogue		47, 48	32, 33, 34	29, 30, 32, 34	30, 31, 32, 33, 34
Syllabication			44, 45, 48	43, 48	47, 48
Synonyms			47, 48	8	27
Verbs/Root words in verbs	38, 39, 40, 41, 42, 43, 48	34	17, 19, 20, 21, 22, 23, 26	19, 20	42, 48
Verb tenses			20, 26	21, 26	14, 18
Vowels	47, 48	12, 13			

Contents

Editors: Alison Millar and Alison MacTier   Cover image: Barrie Richardson
Layout artist: Suzanne Ward   Cover design: Kim Ashby and Design for Marketing, Ware

© 1996 Folens Limited, on behalf of the authors.
Every effort has been made to contact copyright holders of material used in this book. If any have been overlooked, we will be pleased to make any necessary arrangements.

British Library in Publication Data. A catalogue record for this book is available from the British Library.

First published 1996 by Folens Limited, Dunstable and Dublin.
Folens Limited, Albert House, Apex Business Centre, Boscombe Road, Dunstable, LU5 4RL, England.

ISBN 1 85276233 0

Printed in Singapore by Craft Print.

Three rules for sentences

1. A sentence begins with a **capital letter**.

2. A sentence ends with a **full stop**.

3. A sentence makes **sense**.

Example: The sun is shining today.

A Write four **sentences** about each picture.

B Read your sentences to a partner.
Let him or her check it against the three rules.

Full stops

A No-one can understand Enid's story because she never uses **full stops**. Where should Super Stop make his mark?

Write Enid's story correctly and finish it for her.
Remember the **full stops**.

> The giant crept up behind me I was
>
> scared stiff I could feel his breath on
>
> the back of my neck I decided to make
>
> a run for it He chased me along High
>
> Street and into the shop I rushed to
>
> the checkout and ...

B Proofread and correct the story.

Writing sentences

A Write these sentences correctly. Put in the **captial letters** and **full stops**.

1. once upon a time there lived a poor man who had two sons
2. he was the best runner and footballer in Yorkshire
3. the farmer took the sheep to the fair
4. the robbers hid the gold in the cave
5. my friend and I were picked for the team
6. the big game will be played in March
7. next Saturday is the last day of the month
8. the girls felt very homesick in Paris

B There are two **sentences** in each of the following. Write them correctly. Put in the **capital letters** and **full stops**.

1. the sick man was taken to hospital he was kept there for the night
2. it was a cold, wet day today tomorrow will be sunny
3. he felt hungry and stopped to eat his lunch a lady came by and spoke to him
4. the holidays came at last the children were delighted
5. she got a new watch for her birthday it was made in Japan
6. the leaves were falling from the trees we went to the woods to collect chestnuts
7. when the dogs came, the rabbits ran away we did not see them again
8. the fairy granted a wish to the prince his wish came true

A bad day at school

A   Match the **beginnings** and **endings** of the **sentences**.
Use the **sentences** to write a story.

Beginnings	Endings
1. Today I had	and left it at home.
2. I could not write	I spilled paint everywhere.
3. I forgot my reading book	for talking too much.
4. I got knocked over	a bad day at school.
5. My jumper got muddy	on my sandwiches.
6. By accident I sat	because I broke my pencil.
7. By accident	when I fell in a puddle.
8. My team lost	in the playground.
9. I got told off	and was late home.
10. I missed the bus	when we played games.

B   Write four different answers that Meera could give.

Hello Meera. What did you do at school today?

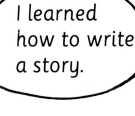

I learned how to write a story.

Gran's birthday

Use the words in the boxes to finish the **sentences** and tell the story.

1. Yesterday was Gran's [   ].
   She was fifty-five years [   ].
   She got lots of [   ] and presents.

   | candles |
   | birthday |
   | cards |
   | old |

2. Gran got a new [   ] and a pair of [   ].
   She [   ] her new jumper very much.

   | slippers |
   | hated |
   | jumper |
   | liked |

3. When she sat [   ] for a cup of [   ] there was a [   ] at the door.

   | round |
   | tea |
   | knock |
   | down |

4. It was the [   ]. There was a [   ] for Gran.
   She was [   ].

   | surprised |
   | dentist |
   | parcel |
   | post |

5. Gran [   ] it and looked inside.
   She [   ].
   It was another [   ]!

   | smiled |
   | jumper |
   | opened |
   | tore |

Basic Rules of Grammar: Book 2

The boy and the wolf

A   Use the words in the box to finish the **sentences** and tell the story.

talk	thought	loudly	angry	village
frightened	no-one	looked	attacking	joke
silly	third	trick	voice	found
play	that	did	ran	people

1. The boy who [_____] after the sheep was fed up. It was a boring job. There was no-one to [_____] to and no-one to [_____] with.

2. The boy [_____] he would have some fun. He pretended [_____] a wolf was [_____]. He shouted [_____] for help.

3. The [_____] from the village [_____] to see what was happening. They were [_____] when they [_____] out it was a [_____].

4. The next day the boy played the same [_____]. The people from the [_____] were fed up with his game.

5. On the [_____] day a wolf really [_____] come. The boy was [_____]. He shouted for help at the top of his [_____], but [_____] came.

B   Make up your own ending for the story.

Test 1

A Match the **beginnings** and **endings** of these **sentences**. Remember the **capital letters** and **full stops**.

1. it was a very hot day   and they hurt his feet

2. simon had some new shoes   for my good work

3. the teacher rewarded me   so I went swimming

B Write this story correctly. Put in the **capital letters** and **full stops**.

a department store has collapsed there is an ambulance nearby police officers are talking to people children are crying.

Write two more **sentences** about the picture.

> Help me finish my notes. Write what you think the missing words might be.

Mr Bloggs said that he was [   ] his van along the High Street when he heard a [   ]. He saw people [   ] and [   ]. There had been a bank [   ]. Two people ran towards a parked [   ] which [   ] down the street. He used his mobile phone to call the [   ]. He [   ] the [   ] of the car.

Common nouns

Nouns are naming words.
Common nouns are the names of things.
Example: The cat was on the table.

A Copy and complete this story with common nouns:

The Search

Once there was a little [＿＿＿]. There was a precious [＿＿＿]

hidden in the woods, so the little [＿＿＿] went to look for it.

Deep between some dark [＿＿＿] and gloomy [＿＿＿]

there was a [＿＿＿]. The little [＿＿＿] crept forward,

frightened about what might happen next. The [＿＿＿]

crunched and the [＿＿＿] swayed. The little [＿＿＿] looked

down and saw a wonderful shiny [＿＿＿]! It was covered with

[＿＿＿] and [＿＿＿]. The little [＿＿＿] lifted it up and

carried it carefully [＿＿＿].

B 1. Copy and complete this chart with common nouns:

	Fruit	Flower	Bird	Drink
c	cherry	carnation	crow	coffee
m	melon	marigold		
p	plum			

2. Continue the chart using the letters 'o' and 'f'.

Common nouns

A List the **common nouns** for 15 things you can see in this picture:

B Copy and complete these sentences with **common nouns**:

1. The ☐ lives in the kennel.

2. The ☐ brings our letters.

3. A ☐ lives in a cave.

4. A ☐ is used for eating.

5. I keep my money in the ☐ .

6. There are nice flowers in their ☐ .

7. The ☐ walked into the classroom.

8. He lost the ☐ on the beach.

Proper nouns

The names of months and days are **proper nouns**.
They begin with **capital letters**.

January	June	November	Thursday
February	July	December	Friday
March	August	Monday	Saturday
April	September	Tuesday	Sunday
May	October	Wednesday	

A Which months could these pictures show?

B Complete these sentences with the **proper nouns** for months or days:

1. [　　　] is the day after Monday.

2. [　　　] is the eleventh month of the year.

3. [　　　] is the month with the fewest letters in it.

4. [　　　] has the fewest number of days.

5. [　　　] is the first month of the year.

6. [　　　] ends with 'st'.

7. [　　　] was named after Julius Caesar.

8. [　　　] is the day that has the most letters in its name.

Proper nouns

The names of people, places, days, months, brands and special occasions are **proper nouns**.
They begin with **capital letters**.

A List the **proper nouns** in this box:

street	Ms Mitten	Adidas	bush
ghost	Southampton	Mr Crystal	North Street
Germany	chair	planet	coach
computer	Roberta	Mars	Id-ul-Fitr

B Copy and complete this **proper noun** chart.
Add nine more lines to the chart.

Person	Place	Brand name	Day, month or special occasion
Yusuf	California	Coca cola	Monday
Mr Roberts	Wales	Nintendo	August
Elvis Presley	Elm Avenue	Rover	Divali

C Write these sentences correctly. Put in the **capital letters** for the **proper nouns**.

1. mrs brown is married to mr brown.

2. john lives in glasgow.

3. angela's birthday is in june.

4. mairi's mother has a new ford fiesta.

5. christopher is canadian.

6. christmas is in december.

7. joshua is going skiing in the swiss alps.

Singular and plural

Singular means only **one**.
Plural means **more than one**.

We say one **cat** but two **cats**.
We say one **box** but two **boxes**.
We say one **church** but two **churches**.

A Copy and complete these sentences with **plurals**:

1. We say one girl but two [   ] .

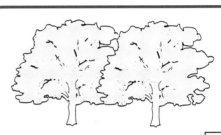

2. We say one tree but two [   ] .

3. We say one glass but two [   ] .

 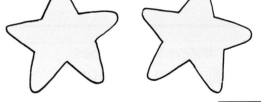

4. We say one star but two [   ] .

B Write the **plurals** of these words:

1.	fox	2.	dish
3.	watch	4.	match
5.	bush	6.	beach
7.	class	8.	coach
9.	bone	10.	cake
11.	head	12.	pass
13.	wish	14	dash
15.	box	16.	stone

Here come the pronouns

Pronouns can be used instead of **nouns**.
Examples: Asma gave her pencil to Julie.
          She gave **it** to Julie.
          She gave **it** to **her**.

A Re-write these sentences about Kenneth and Angie.
Replace the **nouns** with **pronouns**.

 This is Kenneth. **Kenneth** is eight. **Kenneth's** sister is called
Angie. **Angie** is very bossy. **Angie's** teacher complains that
Angie talks too much. Kenneth and Angie play together.
Kenneth and Angie are always playing tricks on people.

B Copy these sentences.
Underline the **pronouns**.

me	he	her	it	we
us	them	you		

1. We went to Wales last week.

2. Peter gave me his books.

3. There are two people with them.

4. Let us go to France.

5. Will you sit next to me?

6. We will see you next week.

7. He is coming in the car with us.

8. Alison gave them to her.

Animal sounds and movements

A Write two sentences about each animal.

Choose **verbs** from the box to write about the sound that they make and how they move.

grunts	croaks	bleats	neighs	brays	howls
lion	monkey	trumpets	prowls	chatters	climbs
elephant	mouse	squeaks	scampers	roars	ambles

B Copy and complete this animal sounds chart.
The **verbs** in the box in **A** will help.

Animal	Sound
elephant	trumpets
monkey	
lion	
mouse	
wolf	
pig	
frog	
donkey	
horse	
lamb	

Continue the chart with some more animals and their sounds.

Test 2

A Copy and complete these sentences with **common nouns**:

1. Sometimes I like to read a [b   ] .

2. A [s   ] is something I like to eat.

3. I go to [s   ] to learn.

4. I like to have a good soak in the [b   ] .

5. I keep my hair tidy with a [c   ] .

6. I like to listen to [m   ] .

B Write your name and address. Remember to use **capital letters** for all **proper nouns**.

C Write the **plurals** of these words:

1. fox   2. book   3. brush   4. finger   5. beach

D Copy and complete the story with the **pronouns** in the box.

she	they	he	her

Mrs Patel went to the shop with [   ] baby son.

When [   ] was in the shop Mrs Patel met [   ]

friend. While [   ] were talking the baby grabbed some

tins from a shelf. As [   ] all fell down with a crash [   ]

smiled and chuckled.

Basic Rules of Grammar: Book 2 © Folen

Verbs

Verbs are **doing** words or **being** words.
Example: It **was** sunny so we **ran** and **played** outside.

A Copy and complete this story with **verbs**.
Underline the **verbs**.

 **The Pond**

There ☐ a pond in the park. Tony and Nicky ☐

down the slope and ☐ into the green depths. Nicky

☐ on the mud and ☐ into the water! His feet

☐ covered with slime. Tony ☐ . Then Nicky

☐ out of the pond and ☐ up the bank. To his

surprise, he ☐ a frog sitting in his jam jar. The boys ☐

back across the park to ☐ their friends the frog.

B Copy and complete this **verb** chart:

Animal	Verb
snake	slithers
mole	
kangaroo	
butterfly	
snail	
bull	

C Write four different **verbs** for ways that people move.

In the past

Verbs are changed to show what has already happened.
We call this the **past tense**.

Examples: Today – **present tense**
The boy **runs**.
The dog **barks**.
The ball **is rolling**.

Yesterday – **past tense**
The boy **ran**.
The dog **barked**.
The ball **was rolling**

A Copy these sentences.
Underline the **verbs** in the **past tense**.

1. The cat chased the mouse.

2. The farmer bought a new horse.

3. The bus was coming down the road.

4. The light was shining in the dark.

5. Her brother fell and broke his arm.

6. The cow jumped over the moon.

7. A small bird sang in the tree.

B Copy and complete these sentences with
verbs in the **past tense**:

1. The baby ☐ all night.

2. The police ☐ the robber.

3. The lion ☐ the deer.

4. A tree ☐ in our garden.

5. Peter ☐ a long letter.

6. The old man ☐ the dog a bone.

7. His uncle ☐ in Exeter.

8. The Irish team ☐ the match.

Basic Rules of Grammar: Book 2

© Folens

The seaside

A   Look carefully at the picture and then at the **18** statements.
Are they true or false?

Write your answers like this:

1. Someone is sleeping. (True)

Someone is ...

1. sleeping	2. drawing	3. kicking a ball
4. reading	5. drowning	6. sun bathing
7. hopping	8. fishing	9. sharing
10. swimming	11. shooting	12. crying
13. sailing	14. drinking	15. knitting
16. paddling	17. eating	18. smiling

B   1. Write six true sentences about your class.

2. Write six false sentences about your class.

A choice of words

Is or Are

We write **is** when we speak of **one**.
We write **are** when we speak of **more than one**.
You is an exception and is always written **you are**.

A Copy these sentences.
Write **is** or **are** in the spaces.

1. Yasmin and Jimmy [   ] playing in the garden.
2. Her face [   ] clean but her hands [   ] dirty.
3. She [   ] crying because her knees [   ] cut.
4. When the cat [   ] asleep, the mice [   ] awake.
5. His cheeks [   ] swollen and his nose [   ] broken.
6. These [   ] the paints Mary [   ] using.
7. You [   ] fond of cats but Tom [   ] not.
8. While Sonia [   ] playing, Depak and Peter [   ] reading.
9. The gatekeeper [   ] going to show us a secret tunnel.

Was or Were

We write **was** when we speak of **one**.
We write **were** when we speak of **more than one**.
You is an exception and is always written **you were**.

B Copy these sentences.
Write **was** or **were** in the spaces.

1. The foreman [   ] angry and the workers [   ] worried.
2. She [   ] wrong and you [   ] right.
3. James [   ] at the shops but his mother [   ] at home.
4. It [   ] night and we [   ] far from home.
5. While they [   ] fishing I [   ] picking sea shells.
6. The socks [   ] red and the coat [   ] green.
7. John [   ] happy when the cats [   ] purring.
8. The girl [   ] crying but her friend [   ] laughing.
9. I [   ] writing while you [   ] reading.

What is it for?

A Write a sentence about what each object is used for.
When a **verb** ends in **e**, you need to take off the **e** before adding **ing**.

Example: A pencil is for writ**ing**.

shave	write	bite	drive	give
shine	ring	shake	bounce	cook

1. ball

2. present

3. razor

4. alarm clock

5. oven

6. maracas

7. pencil

8. car

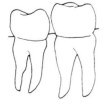

9. teeth

10. torch

B List six parts of a car.
Write a sentence about each one.
Say what it is for.

Questions

Some sentences ask **questions**.
These words ask a **question**.

where?   **who?**   **why?**
what?   **when?**   **how?**

A **question** must have a **question mark** at the end.

A   Write these sentences with **question marks** or **full stops** at the end:

1. Where is your sister today
2. I love apples and oranges
3. How is your grandmother
4. We play football on Saturday
5. Who ate my dinner
6. Why is Daddy still in bed
7. John watches too much television
8. What is Amrit eating

B   Write **questions** for these answers.
Use **where, who, why, what, when** and **how**.

1. I finished my homework last night.
2. Saqib did the washing-up.
3. I baked a lovely cake.
4. He went to bed at ten o'clock.
5. Mike did a lot of housework.
6. We walked slowly.
7. We did the exercise yesterday.
8. She ate her lunch quickly.
9. The car is in the garage.
10. I wore a coat because I was cold.

Questions

A Imagine you are a police officer interviewing witnesses.
Write a **question** for each answer.
There are two **questions** for each picture.

1. I saw two men wearing masks.
They were carrying a ladder,
rope, a hammer and a brick.

2. I heard breaking glass.
I saw a ladder by the wall.

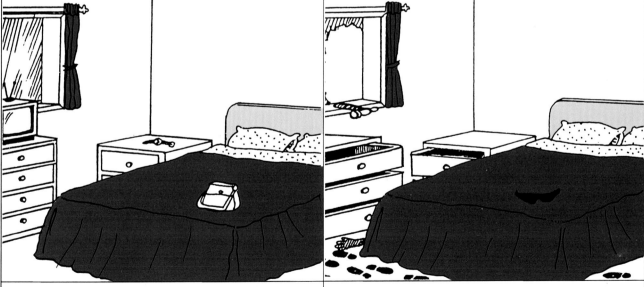

3. They were carrying a television
set. They ran towards town.

4. They left a mask, a hammer
and a glove. They stole clothes,
jewellery, a handbag and the
television.

Test 3

A Copy these sentences. Underline the **verbs**.

1. The bully pushed the small boy over.
2. The dog chased the cat.
3. Humpty Dumpty fell off the wall.
4. The lion roared loudly.
5. On my birthday I had lots of presents.

B Write these sentences using the correct **verb**:

1. The girls **was/were** very noisy.
2. The cat **is/are** hiding from the dog.
3. The workers **was/were** plastering the wall.
4. The teachers **was/were** marking the books.
5. Jane **was/were** writing.

C Copy these sentences. Put in the missing **full stops** or **question marks**.

1. Who are you
2. My father works in a shop
3. What are you going to do after school
4. Can I come and play with your video games
5. I am having beans on toast for tea

D Complete these **questions**:

1. [   ] will you be back from your holiday?
2. [   ] will help me?
3. [   ] do you have a rabbit in your hat?
4. [   ] are you doing?
5. [   ] can I help you?
6. [   ] are you going?

Basic Rules of Grammar: Book 2   © Folens

Alphabetical order

Lists of names are often in **alphabetical order**.
This makes the names easy to find.
Here is the alphabet:

a b c d e f g h i j k l m n o p q r s t u v w x y z

Help Ms Roberts to list the children's names for the class register.

A Put the children's first names in **alphabetical order**.
Look at the first letter of each name.

Georgina	Michael
Amardip	Dawn
Yvonne	Soraya
Christopher	Barry
Ram	Elaine
Joanne	Frederick

B Put their surnames in **alphabetical order**.

Jones	Watson
Moorcroft	Iqbal
Spilling	Harrison
Barker	O'Grady
Patel	Kemp
Dako	Folens

Alphabetical order

Lists, dictionaries and glossaries are often in **alphabetical order**.
This makes the words easy to find.

a b c d e f g h i j k l m n o p q r s t u v w x y z

A   Write these musical instruments in **alphabetical order**.

trombone	oboe	clarinet	horn
drum	guitar	piano	flute
saxophone	violin	bassoon	maracas

Some lists have more than one word that begin with the same letter.

The second letter is important.

Example: c**e**llo, cl**a**rinet

B   Put this list of flowers in **alphabetical order**.
Remember to look at the second letter of each word.

petunia   pansy   poppy   pink   primrose

C   Copy this list of jobs.
Add some more to fill the spaces.
Keep them in **alphabetical order**.

detective, ☐☐☐☐ , drummer, editor, ☐☐☐☐☐ , fire fighter

Adjectives

Adjectives are describing words.
Example: A **fat** cat met a **frightened** mouse on a **cold**, **dark** night.

Copy and complete this story. Fill in the spaces with **adjectives**.

Jack and the Beanstalk

Jack and his mother were ☐ . One ☐ day,

Jack woke up to find a ☐ beanstalk outside his

☐ window. Soon he was climbing up the ☐

stalk, past the ☐ leaves towards the ☐ clouds.

Then he saw a ☐ path leading to a ☐ castle.

He knocked on the ☐ door. A ☐ giant opened

the door and Jack asked for some ☐ food. He was

given ☐ bread, and then the ☐ giant fell asleep.

Jack quickly stole a ☐ hen and some ☐

gold, and tumbled down the ☐ beanstalk.

Jack and his mother were ☐ !

B Copy and complete this chart.
Write two **adjectives** to **describe** each of these **nouns**:

Noun	Adjectives
jelly sand water toffee	wobbly, cold

C Write four **adjectives** to **describe** your friend.

Adjectives

The **little white** kitten played with a **fluffy** ball.

The words **little**, **white** and **fluffy** are **adjectives**.
They tell us more about the kitten and the ball.

Read the different **adjectives** used to **describe** the hen.

a **frightened** hen	a **hungry** hen	a **white** hen	an **angry** hen
a **little** hen	a **fat** hen	a **cackling** hen	an **old** hen

A Copy the sentences.
Underline the **adjectives**.

1. The big dog killed the brown rat.
2. The pretty butterfly landed on the red rose.
3. The grey squirrel cracked a hard nut.
4. The gentle white lamb played in the green field.
5. The rich man bought a big car.
6. The timid mouse ate the fresh cheese.
7. The brown bear lived in the dark woods.
8. The sly fox killed a plump duck.
9. The black beetle crawled under a mossy stone.
10. The small black horse drank the clear water.

B Write an interesting **adjective** to **describe** each picture.

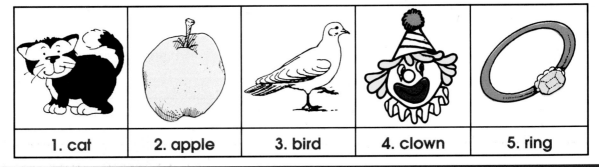

1. cat	2. apple	3. bird	4. clown	5. ring

Basic Rules of Grammar: Book 2 © Folen

Descriptions

Copy the **description** that matches each picture.

1 	Fawzia has long black hair and a round face. She is wearing a spotted dress.
2 	Sam has short, fair hair and wears glasses. He is wearing a tie.
3 	Charlotte has freckles and a snub nose. She is wearing a hat.
4 	Ben has lost some teeth. His hair is curly. He likes wearing t-shirts.
5 	Mark sucks his thumb. He has short black hair and is wearing a scarf.
6 	Mary is always smiling. She has long, fair hair and wears earrings.

Spoken words

In **picture stories** spoken words are shown in **speech bubbles**.
In **text** spoken words are shown in **speech marks**.
The **speech marks** are instead of **speech bubbles**:

Example: The sheep said, "Watch out, here's the farmer."

A   Look at the picture story and read the text.
Copy the story and write in the words that are **spoken**.

	Farmer Trotter was surprised when he entered the kitchen. He shouted, "
	?"
	Farmer Trotter was angry. He called, "
	?"
	He was hopping mad when the sheep answered, "
	?"
	When Farmer Trotter found Boy Blue, he roared, "
	?"

B   Write your own version of Jack and Jill, using **speech marks**.

Basic Rules of Grammar: Book 2

Spoken words

Read this story.
Look for the words that are **spoken**.

The Brave Little Tailor

One morning, a tailor was sitting at his window
working, when an old woman came down the road.
She was crying, "Honey for sale! Honey for sale!"
It was nearly lunch time.
The tailor thought honey would be nice on his bread.
So he put his head out of the window and called,
"Here, my good woman. I'll have some honey."
The old woman hurried over to the tailor, and he
bought some honey.
"I'll spread the honey on a slice of bread," he said to
himself. He put the bread on the table near him and
carried on with his work.

Copy and complete this chart to show who **says** what.

The old woman	The tailor

Test 4

A The astronaut cannot find the instructions in the spaceship handbook.
Put the headings in **alphabetical order**.

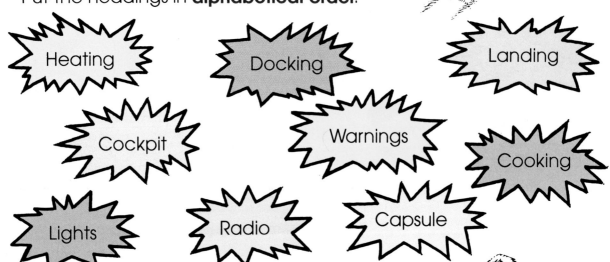

Heating

Docking

Landing

Cockpit

Warnings

Cooking

Lights

Radio

Capsule

B Copy these sentences.
Underline the **adjectives**.

1. The big boy ran up the steep hill.

2. Surinder had some exciting presents for her birthday.

3. The elephant's skin was grey and wrinkly.

4. The noisy children played in the the park.

C Copy these sentences.
Underline the **spoken words**.

1. Jack said, "Please buy my cow."

2. The magician said, "I'll exchange it for these magic beans."

3. "Yes please," said Jack.

4. "You silly boy," said Jack's mother.

Exactly the opposite

Michelle and Michael are twins.
They are also exactly the **opposite**.

A   Write the pairs of **opposites**.

Michelle	Michael
1. soft	1. hard
2. thick	2. ☐
3. easy	3. ☐
4. strong	4. ☐
5. comfortable	5. ☐
6. dry	6. ☐
7. safe	7. ☐
8. ☐	8. sour
9. ☐	9. boring
10. ☐	10. blunt
11. ☐	11. old
12. ☐	12. loud
13. ☐	13. empty

B   List six more pairs of **opposites**.

Antonyms

Words that have **opposite** meanings are called **antonyms**.

A   Copy and complete these sentences with **antonyms** of the red words. Use the words in the box.

soft	big	sweet	light	black
dirty	empty	stale	dull	smooth

1.   The plum is **small** but the apple is ⬚ .
2.   The nut is **hard** but the peach is ⬚ .
3.   The coconut is **rough** but the tomato is ⬚ .
4.   The lemon is **bitter** but the pear is ⬚ .
5.   The marrow is **heavy** but the cherry is ⬚ .
6.   The melon is **clean** but the grape is ⬚ .
7.   The new potato is **white** but the plum is ⬚ .
8.   The orange is **bright** but the fig is ⬚ .
9.   The bowl is **full** of fruit but the bag is ⬚ .
10. The lettuce is **fresh** but the loaf of bread is ⬚ .

B   A strange tale.
Re-write this story, replacing the red words with their **antonyms**:

Jack and Jill

One **night** Jack and Jill went **down** a hill. They carried a **full** bucket. "Why can't we just turn **off** a tap like **nobody** else?" asked Jack. They **emptied** the bucket with **dirty** water and **uncovered** it. The well was **shallow** and it was too **light** to see the **top** of it. "This is the **first** time I'm coming **down** here!" said Jill.

Odd one out

A Which is the odd one out in each line?

1.	lion	monkey	car	elephant
2.	crab	butterfly	snail	tortoise
3.	apple	sock	coat	t-shirt
4.	house	cat	flat	school	hotel
5.	tree	table	kettle	bed	bath
6.	teapot	kettle	cup	jug	knife
7.	doctor	coat	baker	builder	farmer
8.	red	yellow	banana	orange	green
9.	hat	chin	leg	foot	nose
10.	apple	carrot	orange	pear	banana
11.	bike	boy	car	boat	rocket
12.	run	skip	house	jump	hop

B Write a list of each of the following.
Put an odd one out in each list.

1. fruits   2. games   3. jobs   4.   drinks

Homophones

These three words **sound the same** but they are spelled differently and mean different things. They are called **homophones**.

There is about **place**.

Example: It is over **there**.
There it is!

Their is about **possession**.

Example: **Their** friends came.
They had **their** bikes.

They're is short for **they are**.

Example: **They're** very big fish
and **they're** good to eat.

A Copy and complete these sentences with **there**, **their** or **they're**:

1. The ball is over ☐ .
2. The spacemen went on ☐ mission.
3. ☐ the best runners in the class.
4. The children ate ☐ pizzas.
5. We looked here and ☐ .
6. ☐ very good at dancing.

B Write three sentences of your own using **there**, **their** and **they're**.

Basic Rules of Grammar: Book 2 © Folen

Take a rest – use a comma

A **comma** is a little rest in a sentence.

Examples: To get to the Town Hall, go to the end of First Street, turn right, walk along until you reach the Red Lion Pub, turn left and it is in front of you.

To boil an egg, boil the water, add the egg, cook for three minutes and take it out.

A Copy these sentences. Put in the **commas**.

1. Sam climbed the steps walked along the plank closed his eyes and jumped into the water.

2. Lucy cleaned her teeth brushed her hair washed her face and ran downstairs to meet her friend.

3. Yasmin clamped the wood chose the correct saw marked ten centimetres and cut off the piece.

4. Peter opened a book wrote the date thought about it erased it wrote it again and began his story.

We also use **commas** when we make a list.

Example: Netball, cricket, football, snooker and rugby are games.

B Write a sentence that has a list of:

1. animals
2. drinks
3. boys' names
4. girls' names
5. numbers
6. towns
7. countries

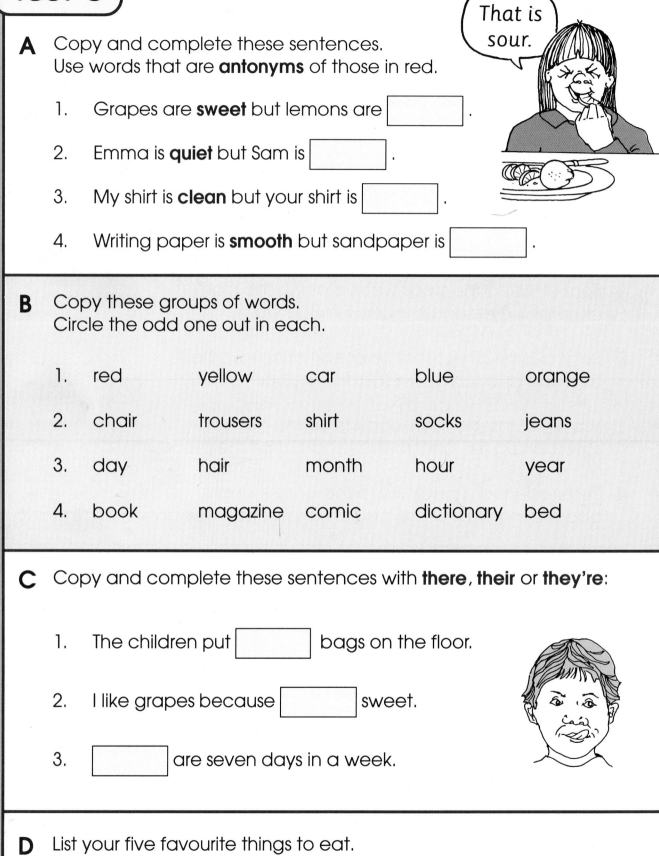

A Copy and complete these sentences.
Use words that are **antonyms** of those in red.

That is sour.

1. Grapes are **sweet** but lemons are [ ] .

2. Emma is **quiet** but Sam is [ ] .

3. My shirt is **clean** but your shirt is [ ] .

4. Writing paper is **smooth** but sandpaper is [ ] .

B Copy these groups of words.
Circle the odd one out in each.

1. red	yellow	car	blue	orange
2. chair	trousers	shirt	socks	jeans
3. day	hair	month	hour	year
4. book	magazine	comic	dictionary	bed

C Copy and complete these sentences with **there**, **their** or **they're**:

1. The children put [ ] bags on the floor.

2. I like grapes because [ ] sweet.

3. [ ] are seven days in a week.

D List your five favourite things to eat.
Remember to put commas in your list.

Adverbs: How do you do it?

Adverbs help to build up description.
An **adverb** can be made by adding **ly** to an **adjective**.

Examples:

How did you do in the test?

Badly!

Neatly!

Awfully!

Beautifully!

A Change these **adjectives** into **adverbs** by adding **ly**:

1. sudden
2. sad
3. quiet

4. careful
5. safe
6. painful

7. loud
8. neat
9. slow

Some **adverbs** do not follow this rule.

Examples: gent**le** – gent**ly**, happ**y** – happ**ily**, dizz**y** – dizz**ily**, angr**y** – angr**ily**.

B Copy and complete these sentences with **adverbs**:

1. Susy sprinted [ ] along the track. (quick)

2. Saqib [ ] put the kitten in its basket. (gentle)

3. The cat [ ] played with the wool. (happy)

4. The top spun [ ]. (dizzy)

5. "Stop that!" shouted Mother [ ]. (angry)

Conjunctions

A **conjunction** is a word used to **join** parts of a sentence.

A Make sure you can read and spell these **conjunctions**.
Ask a friend to read them to you while you write them.
Check your spellings.

or	and	so	but	yet	then
while	however	only	since		therefore
although	because	until	either		neither

B Copy and complete these sentences with **conjunctions** from the box in **A**:

1. I didn't go out [   ] it rained.

2. John went to the shops [   ] Bill stayed in.

3. This flower is white, [   ] this one is red.

4. I will wait for you [   ] five o'clock.

5. The rabbit ate too much, [   ] it got fat.

6. Bill stayed in [   ] John went to the shops.

C Write three more sentences using three different **conjunctions**

Basic Rules of Grammar: Book 2

Prepositions

A **preposition** can show where or when something happens.

in the box

on the box

under the box

Here are some **prepositions**:

above	behind	in	outside
across	below	in front of	over
after	beside	inside	through
against	between	near	to
along	by	next to	towards
around	down	of	under
at	for	on	up
before	from	out	with

A Choose a different **preposition** for each sentence:

My dog was running ☐ the house. Suddenly she went ☐ the road. Soon she went ☐ the trees. Quickly I ran ☐ her. I chased her ☐ a pond. She left the pond and went ☐ the supermarket. She ran ☐ the meat counter! Quickly, I got a bone and rushed ☐ the cash desk. I ran home and put the bone ☐ her basket.

She followed me, and sat ☐ me to enjoy her bone.

B Look at the list of **prepositions**. Find the opposites for as many as you can. Write the pairs of words.

Syllabication

Some words are easier to read if you divide them into **syllables**
Copy the word that matches each picture.
Put a line between the **syllables**.

1. Example		2.	
	con|tent		gossip
	con|test		goblin
	<u>cos|tume</u>		goblet

3.		4.	
	temper		wonder
	tinsel		winner
	thinner		winter

5.		6.	
	public		admit
	plastic		index
	problem		escape

7.		8.	
	triplets		seldom
	tennis		selfish
	trumpet		sandal

9.		10.	
	pistol		sister
	picnic		basket
	napkin		bandit

Basic Rules of Grammar: Book 2

Syllabication

Sometimes two short words are put together to make one longer word. The new word is called a **compound** word.

A   Copy these words.
Draw a line between the two small words.
Example: in/side

1. in/side	2. upset	3. bathtub
4. sunset	5. pancake	6. bathmat
7. hillside	8. homesick	9. handbag
10. bedtime	11. nightmare	12. whiplash
13. bedroom	14. sandbox	15. shotgun
16. maybe	17. classmate	18. campfire
19. keyring	20. flagpole	21. baseball

Sometimes an ending such as **ful**, **less** or **ness** is added to a word to make a new word.
The original word without the ending is called the **root** word.

B   Copy the words and underline the **root** word in each.
Example: **sad**ness.

1. sadness	2. hopeful	3. smokeless
4. useless	5. hopeless	6. stillness
7. helpful	8. useful	9. homeless
10. thankful	11. illness	12. wireless
13. bashful	14. careless	15. mindful
16. skillful	17. wishful	18. likeness
19. cupful	20. artful	21. brightness

Basic Rules of Grammar: Book 2

Prefixes

A **prefix** goes before a word.
Re is a **prefix** meaning **back** or **again**.

Example: **re**turn

A Copy these sentences adding **re** to the words in bold print:

1. They tried to **float** the stranded ship.

2. The salesman said he would **fund** my money.

3. Will you **model** this coat into a new style?

4. The tyres were **moulds** made from old tyres.

5. Please **move** your shoes.

6. I will **build** the wrecked ship.

7. The cashier had to **count** the money.

8. I asked Sam to **hang** the curtains.

B Copy these sentences.
Replace the words in bold with one word starting with **re**.

1. The plumber **came again** to fix the burst pipe.

2. The runners had to **run** the race.

3. The school **opened again** after the mid-term break.

4. The building plans had to be **drawn again**.

5. The broken arm did not set so it had to be **set again**.

6. Mary had to **read** the poem **many times** to learn it.

7. The caged bird had to be **let out** into the wild.

8. I did not like my story so I **wrote** it **again**.

Synonyms

Synonyms are words that **mean the same**.

Example: Rug is a **synonym** for mat.

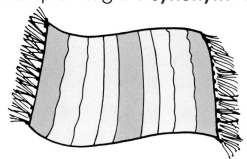

A Write a **synonym** for each word in red.

1. Jane **linked** the two pieces of string with a knot.
2. There is a **gap** between the tables.
3. A **couple** of birds flew past.
4. The children stood in a **row**.
5. The woman **placed** the hammer in the toolbox.
6. The sheep were **munching** grass.

B Copy these sentences.
Replace **get** with a more interesting **synonym**.

1. I am going to **get** a new coat.
2. The cat will **get** on to the high wall.
3. The snakes can **get** under the fence.
4. I cannot **get** the apples at the top of the tree.
5. Please **get** my shoes from the bedroom.
6. Peter will **get** his lost keys.

Basic Rules of Grammar: Book 2

Test 6

A Take **ly** off these **adverbs**. Write the **adjectives** you are left with.

1. sweetly   2. kindly   3. quietly   4. quickly   5. slyly

B Copy and complete these sentences with **conjunctions**:

1. I like toast [   ] it tastes nice.

2. I like apples [   ] I don't like pears.

3. Tom went out to play [   ] came in an hour later.

C Write a **preposition** that is **opposite** in meaning to each of these:

1. down   2. in   3. above   4. behind   5. near

D Copy these **compound** words. Draw a line between the two syllables of each word.
Example: bed/room

1. playground   2. upset   3. football   4. carpet

E Copy these sentences.
Replace the words in red with words stating with **re**.

1. The match ended in a draw and had to be **played again**.
2. The wall had to be **painted again**.
3. I need to **put new strings on** this tennis racquet.

F Write **synonyms** for these words:

1. symbol   2. explode   3. halt

4. leap   5. centre   6. divide